First edition 2018

Copyright © 2018 Anno Domini Publishing
www.ad-publishing.com
Text copyright © 2018 Sally Ann Wright
Illustrations copyright © 2018 Frank Endersby

Published by Authentic Media Ltd
PO BOX 6326, Bletchley, Milton Keynes, MK1 9GG
Conforms to EN71 and AS/NZS ISO 8124

Publishing Director: Annette Reynolds
Art Director: Gerald Rogers
Pre-Production manager: Doug Hewitt

Printed and bound in Malaysia

The story of the first Christmas
And the Star Shone Brightly

Sally Ann Wright
Pictures by Frank Endersby

$\mathcal{A}$ long time ago, in a little village in the hills, the angel Gabriel visited a girl called Mary.

'Don't be afraid,' said the angel. 'God has chosen you to be the mother of his own Son. You will give birth to Jesus, who will come to save all the people of the world.'

Mary trusted God. When the angel left her, she knew that something wonderful would happen.

*M*ary was planning to be married to Joseph, the village carpenter. God told Joseph in a dream to take care of her and her baby. So Joseph married Mary.

When her baby was due to be born, the Roman Emperor ordered a census of all his people. Joseph took Mary to Bethlehem to be counted by the Romans.

*M*ary was tired when they reached the town of Bethlehem. She felt the pains that meant that soon her baby would be born.

Joseph tried to find somewhere for them to stay but everyone had come to Bethlehem to be counted. There were people everywhere. There was no room at the inn.

Joseph found a quiet space away from all the people. It was dark when Mary gave birth to Jesus, her first child. It was a little boy, just as the angel had said. She made a bed for him in a manger full of hay.

And a star shone brightly above them.

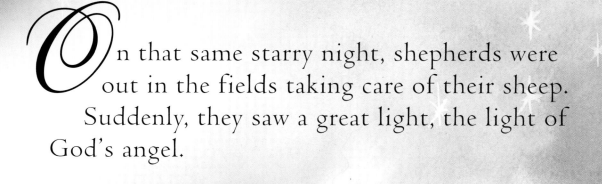

On that same starry night, shepherds were out in the fields taking care of their sheep. Suddenly, they saw a great light, the light of God's angel.

'I have wonderful news!' said the angel.
'Jesus, the one you have been waiting for, has
been born in Bethlehem. Go and find him –
he is lying in a manger.'

Then many thousands of angels came and
sang praises to God.

And a star shone brightly above them.

The shepherds ran to Bethlehem
and found the baby in a manger,
just as the angel had said. They
wondered at this baby who had come to
change the world — and they worshipped him.
And a star shone brightly above them.

A new star appeared in the sky that night.

Wise men in the East saw it. They looked at their charts. They thought about what it might mean.

Could it be that a new king had been born, the king of the Jewish people?

And the star shone brightly above them.

The wise men filled their treasure chests, packing gifts fit for the baby king. They prepared for a long journey and mounted their camels.

And the star shone brightly above them.

*T*ravelling by night, they followed the star.

They travelled from their home in the East through deserts, over the hills and through the valleys until they saw the lights of a town in the distance.

And the star shone brightly above them.

19

When they reached Jerusalem they went to the palace.

'We have come to find the baby king so we may worship him,' they said.

But bad King Herod knew nothing, and he didn't want any other king in his country.

And the star shone brightly above them.

'And where might such a king be born?' Herod asked his advisers.

'In Bethlehem,' they said.

'Come back when you find him,' said Herod to the wise men. 'Perhaps I will also go to worship him…'

And the star shone brightly above them.

The wise men went
on to Bethlehem
until they saw the star
shining over a little house.

They found the child with
his mother, Mary, and gave him
their gifts of gold, frankincense
and myrrh.

And the star shone brightly
above them.

They knelt and worshipped the child, Mary's son, Jesus, the Saviour of the world, the baby king.

Mary wondered at the way that God had blessed her with this precious child.

And the star shone brightly above them.

Then the wise men returned
to their own country by
another way. They had been
told in a dream not to see King
Herod again.

And the star shone brightly
above them.